HONEY, NATURAL

Explains the use of honey as a germ killer, a
harmless sedative, a healer for burns and wounds,
and as a provider of instant energy. Also includes a
varied selection of honey cookery recipes.

HONEY, NATURAL FOOD AND HEALER

by
JANET BORD

SCIENCE OF LIFE BOOKS
4-12 Tattersalls Lane, Melbourne, Victoria 3000

Second edition, revised, enlarged and reset 1983

Registered at the G.P.O. Sydney,
for transmission through the post
as a book.

British Library Cataloguing in Publication Data

Bord, Janet
    Honey, natural food and healer.
    2nd ed., rev & enl.

    1. Honey — Therapeutic use
    I. Title
    615.8'54   RM666.H55

    ISBN 0-909911-01-0

National Library of Australia card number
and ISBN 0 909911 01 0

Printed in Great Britain by
Richard Clay (The Chaucer Press) Ltd,
Bungay, Suffolk

Acknowledgements

The author wishes to thank the following for supplying both information and recipes.

Canada Department of Agriculture

New Zealand Honey Marketing Authority

United States Department of Agriculture

American Honey Institute, 111 East Wacker Drive, Chicago, Illinois 60601

Australian Honey Board, Australia House, Strand, London WC2B 4LA and 647 George Street, Sydney, N.S.W. 2000.

Beekeeping, published by the Devon Beekeepers' Association, 'Woburnia', Seaton Down Road, Seaton, Devon

Contents

Introduction

'The owl and the pussycat went to sea in a
beautiful pea-green boat.
They took some honey and plenty of money
wrapped up in a five-pound note.'

Edward Lear

The owl and the pussycat certainly knew what they
were doing when they decided to take honey with
them on their trip, because it is one of Nature's
most valuable energy-producing foods. Made from
nectar collected by bees from many different kinds
of flowers, honey is a natural sweetener, but it also
contains other constituents which make it a
beneficial food, good for youngsters and adults
alike.

There are unlimited ways in which honey can be
used to add variety, flavour and nutriment to one's
diet, and these will be outlined later, together with
some recipes. But honey is not only valuable as a
food. It has medicinal properties too, and has been
used all over the world, especially in rural areas, for
many centuries to help in the treatment of all kinds
of ailments. It is also used in cosmetics, in wines
and as a preservative, and more and more people, as
they turn away from processed, devitalized and

unnatural foods, are beginning to realize the true importance of honey, a natural, pure, unprocessed food costing relatively little.

Honey and Sugar

How Honey is Produced

'How doth the little busy bee
Improve each shining hour,
And gather honey all the day
From every opening flower!' Isaac Watts

Most people know that honey comes from bees, who themselves produce it from the nectar they collect from the flowers of plants, bushes and trees, but not so many people know the amount of work needed to produce it — between 2 million and 2½ million bee journeys (or 556 bees flying around the world one and a third times) are required to produce one pound of honey!

Every bee colony is highly organized, each bee having his own important part to play. The queen bee (one to a colony) lays around 1500 eggs per day, and when these have become fully developed bees, they learn the tasks of the hive, progressing to more important ones as they grow older. Finally they qualify as scouts, or foragers, leaving the hive to find and collect nectar and pollen. This is taken back to the hive, where the nectar goes through various processes which turn it into honey. So when one considers all the work involved, honey is a very cheap food indeed.

Everyone Likes Honey

Honey was eaten long before bees were domesticated, and in those days men had to go out into the forests, find where the bees were nesting, and rob them of their honey. They went to great lengths to find the trees where the bees had their nests, and sometimes had special tools to help in getting the honey.

Some birds also like honey, but although they know where the honey is to be found, they need a man to help them get it from the nest. In South Africa, the honey-guide leads the natives to the bees' nests and then waits while they take the honey. They always give the bird a share of the honey in payment, for they believe that if they do not, the bird will soon find an opportunity to lead them into danger by way of revenge.

Bears are famed for their fondness for honey, and most people will be familiar with that well-known bear of children's literature, Winnie-the-Pooh, who sang as he climbed up a tree to reach a bees' nest:

> Isn't it funny
> How a bear likes honey?
> Buzz! Buzz! Buzz!
> I wonder why he does?

and who was going to give Eeyore the donkey a pot of honey for his birthday, but unfortunately ate it himself, and so gave him 'a Useful Pot to Keep Things In'.

An amusing old story about the liking for honey of both bear and man, comes from Poland. A man who was searching for honey in the woods fell into a hollow tree and got stuck up to his waist in honey. He was there for two days because no one heard his cries for help. Then, a large bear smelled the honey in the tree, and climbed down on top of the unfortunate man still stuck inside. But the man realized that here was his opportunity for escape, and so he grabbed a tight hold of the bear's fur and began to shout as loudly as he could. The bear, not understanding what was happening, quickly tried to pull himself up out of the tree, and eventually succeeded inadvertently in rescuing the man. Luckily for him, the bear was so frightened that he ran away.

To return to modern times, a story from Slovenia shows that bears are still as keen on honey as they ever were. In the village of Gradec, a brown bear tired to climb a telegraph pole in search of a bees' nest when it mistook the sound of the wind in the overhead wires for bees humming!

What Honey Consists Of

Nectar, when first collected from the flowers, consists mainly of a weak solution of sugar in water. There are sixteen types of sugar present, but two are predominant, levulose (fructose) and dextrose (glucose). At first there is usually more sucrose than levulose and dextrose, but when the nectar is being carried around in the honey stomach of the bees, and in the hive, the enzyme invertase works on the sucrose and changes it into levulose and dextrose.

This is one reason why honey acts so quickly to produce energy, for levulose and dextrose are described as 'pre-digested', and when taken into the body go to work straight away. Ordinary sugar has to be digested by the body first before it can produce energy. Because it is easily digested, honey is of especial value to old people, and also to babies. But anyone who is feeling tired and wants an 'instant lift' without resorting to drugs can take advantage of honey's valuable properties. A couple of teaspoons of honey eaten 'neat', or the same mixed with hot water and drunk, will quickly help to overcome mental or physical tiredness. Of course this recipe should not be considered as a substitute for proper night-time sleep!

Another thing which happens to the nectar in the hive is that the large amount of water gradually evaporates, until in the 'ripe' honey there is usually about 17% moisture. The sugars take up approximately 76% (levulose 40%, dextrose 34%, sucrose 2%), and the remaining 7% is made up of other items such as iron, lime, sodium, sulphur, magnesium, silica, chlorine, potassium, phosphorus, pollen, manganese, aluminium, calcium, copper, albumen, dextrine, nitrogen, proteins, acids and amino acids.

All the percentages given are approximate, because the composition of honey depends on many factors, including what flowers the nectar comes from, the season of the year when it is collected, the weather at the time of collection, and the nature of the soil where the plants grow. It has been found that when they are given a choice, bees prefer to gather nectar from the flowers of plants grown on natural, organically fertilized soil, rather than those grown on chemically fertilized soil. Of course the type of flowers from which the nectar was collected greatly influences the flavour of the honey, and its colour.

The minerals contained in honey come direct from the soil, and all of them are essential to our health. The highest mineral content is found in the darker honeys, which sometimes contain four times as much iron as lighter honeys.

Some vitamins are found in honey, including vitamin C and most of the vitamin B complex. The vitamin C is in the pollen from the flowers, which is a very rich source of this vitamin. Therefore honeys containing a lot of pollen are rich in vitamin C, and this is not lost as quickly from honey as it is from fruit and vegetables. However, honey that has been strained, filtered or overheated in order to remove the pollen (which makes honey look cloudy, an attribute not appreciated by many housewives) is almost totally lacking in vitamin C.

In fact, we are still finding things out about honey. No one yet knows everything there is to know about this valuable food, although it has been with us for thousands of years.

Colour and Flavour

When a bee is collecting nectar, he will usually concentrate on one species of flower at a time. He will choose a flower which is in great profusion in the area where he is working, because this saves time. If that flower is very abundant in the area near the hive, probably most of the other bees will choose the same type of flower, and so that particular batch of honey will be from one recognizable flower source.

The type of flower dictates the colour and flavour of the honey, and these can vary considerably. Some honeys are very light and delicate, and some are dark and quite strong. Clover honey is a light, mild honey; buckwheat honey, produced in the United States and parts of Europe, is an example of a really dark and strong honey. It has a distinctive flavour and is an acquired taste, only really popular in the areas where buckwheat is grown and where the people are used to it.

Not all honey sources are identified, though, and much 'blended' honey is sold. However this is just as good in quality as honeys where the flower source is known.

Most honey is sold on its own after extraction from the comb, but comb honey can also be bought. Most extracted honey is in liquid form, and this may crystallize or 'set' if kept for any length of time. Crystallized honey will easily liquefy again if heated gently in a closed container placed over or in warm water. It should never be heated over an open flame, for overheating changes the characteristics and flavour of honey.

Another form in which honey is now being sold is 'creamed', 'whipped', 'candied', 'fondant' or 'spread', when liquid and crystallized honey are whipped together. In this form, the honey is smooth and soft, spreads easily, and is increasing in popularity because it is easier to handle than runny honey.

White Sugar is Harmful

Our ancestors were lucky enough to live before the days of devitalized foods. They were particularly lucky that white sugar did not form part of their diet because, believe it or not, white sugar is both harmful and addictive.

Many people prove for themselves, when they try to slim, that they take excess sugar without thinking about it. We all know that sugar makes us fat, and so the first step in slimming is usually to give up sugar in coffee and tea, and sweets and cakes, especially cream cakes. Many people who stop taking sugar in coffee and tea soon realize that they can now actually *taste* the coffee and tea, while before all they could taste was the sickly sweetness of the sugar.

Sugar is added to many foods which don't really need sweetening at all, and once your tastebuds have reaccustomed themselves to acutally tasting foods again, you will be able to eat all kinds of stewed fruits, cooking apples, etc., perfectly happily without the addition of the poisonous white sugar. But if you really must have a sweetener, use honey, molasses or raw Barbados sugar. Honey can be substituted for sugar in almost all recipes, as will be demonstrated further in the receipe section.

Why is white sugar so harmful? It has been

refined so much that there is no goodness left in it. It does not promote extra energy (honey is far better for that), and is often indigestible. The increase in ill-health throughout the so-called 'civilized' world has come at a time when more refined and chemical foods are being consumed in place of whole, natural foods, and white sugar and white flour are two of the major culprits.

As regards immediately noticeable effects, white sugar causes overweight. Most people today are overweight; just take a look around when you are next out of doors, and you will be shocked to see just how many people could benefit by losing quite a few pounds.

White sugar is also guilty of speeding up tooth decay, as we well know to our children's cost. Most children are brought up to eat and enjoy foods which are far too sweet, with the result that their teeth decay very rapidly, and they often find themselves wearing dentures before they reach their twenties. This is a deplorable state of affairs, which can easily be remedied. And fluoride in the drinking water is not the answer either. Cutting out sugar completely from the diet and replacing it with honey and molasses, together with a general re-placement of convenience foods with natural foods and raw fruits and vegetables, will go a long way towards ensuring that we keep our own teeth for the best part of our lives. Given the ideal diet from birth, one should still have one's own teeth at death.

A great number of people suffer from sugar addiction, though they probably don't realize it. When sugar is taken into the stomach, a digestive 'explosion' takes place, while the body works hard to deal with the substance. Immediate stimulation is caused, but this soon wears off, causing more harmful sugar to be eaten in order to produce more 'energy'. Malnutrition, diabetes, fatigue, kidney disease and indigestion are only a few of the unpleasant results of sugar addiction. Honey does not have the same violent reaction in the stomach, and does not cause a craving for more. Neither is its use likely to cause all manner of insidious bodily ills.

Saccharine and Glucose

Because they cannot do without sugar, many people use saccharine to sweeten their tea and coffee when they decide to try and slim. This is a very dangerous procedure because saccharine is a drug, and is claimed by many people to be injurious to health, for it is derived from coal tar, a cancer-producing substance. It is interesting that although saccharine is 500 times sweeter than sugar, it is avoided by bees, ants, and flies, all insects which love sugar. They seem to know instinctively which 'foods' are harmful to them. Saccharine is used as a sweetener in many manufactured products, and this should be stated on the label, where you will find it in the list of ingredients.

Glucose is another form of artificial sugar which is presented as being energy-giving and good to take. Many manufactured foods contain glucose, but, like all synthetic products, it should be avoided wherever possible. Honey has all the advantages without the disadvantages.

Honey for Health

A Germ-killer

As well as being the best natural sweetener, honey has important health-giving properties. It is a valuable addition to anyone's diet, because it contains so many minerals and vitamins which are essential to us all. Each of its components has its own part to play in maintaining our health, and they do this even though they are present in such minute, and one would think unimportant, quantities.

Honey is able to absorb moisture from anything with which it comes into contact, even metal and stone. All life needs moisture to survive, and this includes bacteria, so honey can kill even the more harmful bacteria by drawing from them the life-giving moisture.

A bacteriologist who did not believe that honey would kill bacteria tested it, and discovered to his amazement that the disease germs which he placed in pure honey were eventually killed off. The typhoid fever germs died within forty-eight hours, germs causing chronic broncho-pneumonia died after four days, dysentery-producing germs died in ten hours, and numerous other germs were eliminated equally quickly.

A Harmless Sedative

Honey also has a calming effect, and if taken regularly will greatly help the highly-strung, nervy individual. For this purpose, a teaspoonful should be taken six times a day.

Honey's sedative properties are also of value for those who suffer from insomnia, for it can also be used to promote healthy sleep. Just take honey in a warm drink shortly before going to bed, and you will soon find yourself feeling sleepy. One to two teaspoonsful can be stirred into a cup of slightly warmed milk (all the valuable properties of milk are killed if it is boiled or overheated), or added to an equal amount of cider-apple vinegar in half a cup of warm water, or taken in warm water alone. All these drinks are pleasant, but the cider-apple vinegar/honey combination is the most nutritious because cider-apple vinegar is another natural food which should be an integral part of everyone's diet.

If you do not like a drink at bedtime, try taking a tablespoonful of honey with the last meal of the day.

Digestion

As I have said before, the sugar in honey is predigested, and this makes it particularly valuable for people with weak digestions. Ordinary sugars must be converted into simple sugars when they are in the intestine, and this brought about by the action of enzymes. But with honey, this has already been done by a secretion from the bee's salivary glands.

So when we eat honey, it is absorbed easily and quickly, and unlike many foods in the normal diet, does not irritate the lining of the digestive tract. It promotes the correct working of the digestive organs, and acts as a natural laxative. It should therefore be taken regularly by anyone who suffers from constipation (along with an increased amount of raw fruits and vegetables). Alternatively, a mixture of honey and molasses (half of each) can be used as a laxative, this combination also providing vitamins and iron.

Honey in Ill-health

Honey will help to alleviate many painful conditions, and different people claim that it has helped them to get rid of a great variety of illnesses. The answer seems to be, if you are suffering from anything, try honey!

Coughs can be alleviated by honey drinks, and the following should be tried straight away in order to bring relief.

Bronchial Cough Mix equal parts of honey and fresh lemon juice.

Feverish Cough 30 ml (1 fl oz) each of honey, olive oil, lemon juice and sweet spirits of nitre. Take several times a day in half fluid drachm doses.

Obstinate Cough Mix equal quantities of honey, linseed oil and whisky. Take a tablespoonful three or four times a day.

A teaspoonful of heated honey taken alone will often stop a cough quickly, and seems to be especially effective at night.

Colds benefit from the cider-apple vinegar/honey drink described on page 18, together with regular doses of extra vitamin C, especially in the form of rose hip tablets.

Honey drinks are also prescribed for *sore and irritated throats*. Try the following. Mix a gargle of 1 litre (2 pints) water, 125 g honey and 25 g alum.

(This gargle also helps ulcers in the mouth.)

Also for irritated throats, mix 2 tablespoonsful honey, 2 tablespoonsful glycerine, 1 tablespoonful lemon juice and a dash of ginger. Keep the mixture warm and use a little as needed.

Honey and warm milk, as well as being a pleasant drink helps clear husky throats.

According to Dr D.C. Jarvis in his best-selling paperback *Folk Medicine*, honeycomb is even better for breathing tract disturbances than honey, though of course honey should be taken if honeycomb is not immediately available.

It seems that the list of ailments which have in one case or another been alleviated by honey is almost endless. Both arthritis and rheumatism have been helped by honey, as have muscle cramps and twitching. Some people claim that an improved diet, including raw foods and honey, has eliminated tuberculosis; others claim equally amazing results for honey in cases of gastric and intestinal ulcers.

Beekeepers are said to be among the healthiest people in the world (providing they eat their own product, of course). One says, 'Having kept bees and eaten honey for over thirty years, I can tell about my own experience and also give observations of other people who use honey exclusively for sweetening. I have never known a beekeeper who had any kind of kidney trouble. They all have a clear complexion, good eyesight, and no lameness. Among my friends who eat honey and keep bees, there is no cancer or paralysis. My best remedy for a bee sting is to cover it with honey, even a deep burn will not scar if treated the same way. I have seen sour milk, whole wheat cracked for cereal, honey and butter do wonders in diet.'

Doctors have found honey to be valuable for the heart. Dr G.N.W. Thomas in an article in the *Lancet* said, 'in heart weakness I have found honey to have a marked effect in reviving the heart action and keeping patients alive.' The heart is a muscle and, like all our muscles, is stimulated by honey which provides the energy needed by tired muscles.

Honey and lemon tea is recommended for combating *liver disorders*, *skin blemishes*, and as a night-time drink to avoid a cold which threatens. It consists of a tablespoon of honey dissolved in a cupful of hot water, to which the juice of half a lemon is added.

A honey and yarrow drink, comprising a spoonful of honey added to an infusion of yarrow, is sometimes prescribed for *influenza* and as a nourishing tonic. It should be drunk hot at bedtime and first thing in the morning.

A cure for *chilblains* can be made from one tablespoonful each of honey and glycerine, mixed with an egg-white and enough flour to make a fine paste. This paste is then spread over the chilblains, making sure that the skin is clean and dry before application, and the areas affected should afterwards be protected by a cloth because the paste is rather sticky. This recipe claims to relieve and generally cure bad chilblains after a single application.

As a general tonic, the following drink, taken three times a day, is recommended. Mix well together equal parts of honey, cod liver oil, fresh lemon juice and fresh orange juice.

Burns and Wounds
Honey should be applied in cases of burns, for it

keeps the air away from the skin, helps to lessen the pain, and stops blisters forming. Also, the burned area heals much quicker if honey has been used.

Honey will also stop bleeding by causing rapid coagulation of the blood. Ulcers and other skin wounds can also be helped by the application of honey, as can bee stings.

Equal parts of honey and glycerine, mixed together and applied to bruises, helps them heal quicker. This mixture is also recommended for rough skin, chafing, and chaps on hands and face.

In the words of the Greek physician Hippocrates, who advocated the use of honey in the fourth century BC 'It causes heat, cleans sores and ulcers, softens hard ulcers of the lips, heals carbuncles and running sores.'

Honey for Children
All children like honey, and it should feature in their diet every day, right from the earliest days. Mother's milk is the natural food for all babies, and those mothers who for whatever reason cannot feed their babies themselves should make sure that pure honey features in their babies' diets. One to two teaspoonsful should be added to eight ounces of feed, though if the baby becomes constipated, add an extra half-teaspoonful (reduce the amount by half a teaspoonful if the baby suffers from looseness of the bowels). Babies whose diet includes honey rarely suffer from colic.

A bugbear for mothers is bed-wetting, which afflicts many children at some stage or other. Honey can help here too, through its ability to absorb and hold moisture. If a child is given a teaspoonful of honey at bedtime, it will calm his system and reduce the likelihood of there being a wet bed in the morning.

At no stage should a child be given sugar in his diet. His development will be retarded, and he will be more likely to be prone to many unnecessary illnesses, both as a child and when he reaches adulthood. As Dr Seale Harris so vividly puts it, 'The sugar-fed child often becomes rachitic [suffering from rickets], is prone to acquire colitis and other infections. If he survives infancy he becomes the pale, weak, undernourished child, or the fat, flabby, indolent and self-indulgent adolescent.'

More specifically, 'sugar-saturated' children tend to suffer from the following ailments: flatulence, hyperacidity, headaches, restlessness, irritability, decayed teeth, constipation alternating with diarrhoea, rheumatism, bronchitis, eczema, heartburn, persistent head colds, enlarged tonsils and bronchial asthma. I do not think any parents would wish these upsets on their children, which could all be easily avoided by the simple substitution of honey for sugar.

An Age-old Cure

'*Honey is a remedy for all diseases*' Mohammed. As well as being known and loved as a food since time immemorial, honey has also been used for medicinal purposes for many centuries. It was popular in ancient China, India, Persia, Arabia, Assyria, Greece, the Roman Empire and all over Europe, and its use is documented in ancient books. All its medicinal uses today which I have mentioned also applied in past centuries.

But the ancients went even further than we do today, for they also used dead bees! For example, to help with eye disorders Marcellus recommended: 'The honey pure and neat wherein the Bees are dead, let that drop into the eyes; or honey mixt with the ashes of the heads of Bees, makes the eyes very clear.'

A similar prescription is given by Galen for curing baldness. 'Take Bees dead in combs, and when they are through dry make them into powder, mingle them with the honey in which they died and anoint the parts of the Head that are bald and thin-haired, and you shall see them grow again.'

Honey in Cosmetics

Honey and beeswax form the basis of many skin creams, lipsticks and hand lotions, and a useful honey paste which rejuvenates dry hands can be made at home by mixing together the white of an egg, a teaspoonful of glycerine, an ounce of honey and enough barley flour to make a paste. This can be kept in the refrigerator and used as needed.

A beeswax cold cream can also be made quite easily, as follows. Melt 50 g (2 oz) white beeswax in 140 ml (6 fl oz) light liquid paraffin, and bring to a temperature of 50°C (120-145°F), preferably in a double saucepan. Heat 120 ml (4 fl oz) distilled water, and mix in 4 g (⅛ oz) borax. Bring to a temperature slightly above that of the beeswax and oil mixture. Pour the water mixture into the beeswax and paraffin oil mixture (both mixtures should be about the same temperature), and stir continuously, slowing the stirring as the cream thickens and emulsifies. If desired, perfume may be added while stirring.

A facepack can be made by mixing honey with a half-cup of bran to form a smooth paste. (If it is too

thick, add a little rose-water.) Clean the face
thoroughly, then spread the honey paste on quite
thickly. Leave for thirty minutes. Remove with
warm water and a soft cloth, and apply a good
astringent or skin tonic. If used twice a week, this
facepack will keep the skin soft, supple, and free
from scaliness.

Pollen and Royal Jelly

Honey is not the only product of the hive which can
be used beneficially by man. Honeycomb and
beeswax are both valuable, but pollen and royal
jelly are extremely important aspects of the bees'
activity.

The bees collect pollen and nectar from the
flowers, both of which are taken back to the hives to
be used as food. Pollen is very rich in protein, and
without it the bees are unable to perform their tasks
properly. In fact, they cannot live without a supply
of pollen. The same is obviously not true of man,
but it has been found that the taking of pollen in the
diet (it is available in tablet form, or mixed with
honey, from health stores) promotes health and
energy, and this is particularly applicable to those
who are convalescing after an illness.

Pollen has also been found to give relief for
certain ailments, including cerebral haemorrhage,
rickets, anaemia, weight loss, enteritis, colitis, toxic
elimination, constipation, insomnia, lack of appe-
tite, and depression.

Royal jelly is a jelly-like honey which is eaten by
the queen bee. When eaten by man, it gives
strength and energy, but it is claimed by some to be
not so efficacious as pollen. Royal jelly has been
found valuable in the treatment of certain heart
complaints.

Honeycomb

Chewing honeycomb has been found of value for allergies, such as hayfever, which affect the breathing, and in fact for all nasal and sinus complaints. The effect is almost immediate, and a stuffy nose will be cleared very quickly once honeycomb is chewed.

Dr D.C. Jarvis, author of *Folk Medicine*, reports, 'Folk medicine is authority for the finding that individuals who had comb honey in their diet until they reached their sixteenth year seldom have a cold, hay fever, or other nose disorders. It also teaches that the chewing of honeycomb creates an immunity to breathing-tract conditions that lasts for four years.' He also adds that those who have not previously taken honeycomb regularly can also obtain benefit from it if they start using it at a later date.

Those who suffer from hay fever do so regularly every year, and so they should arrange to chew honeycomb daily for a month before they expect attacks to begin. They will in this way either avoid an attack completely, or it will be much milder than usual. During an attack, honeycomb should be taken daily throughout, and it is advisable to continue to chew honeycomb at regular intervals afterwards, as an investment for the following year. A teaspoonful of honeycomb is about the right amount to take at one time — or however much leaves as much comb in the mouth as there would be if you were chewing gum. This should be chewed for fifteen minutes, and then whatever remains should be thrown away.

Bee Venom

Even the bee's weapon, its sting, may have some medicinal value. It was a traditional belief among European peasants that bee stings would cure arthritis and rheumatism, but any modern claims for this remain controversial. It could certainly be a dangerous treatment to try, if the patient happened to be allergic to bee venom. One person in several thousand is allergic to bee venom, and each sting they receive makes the sensitivity worse, until in the end a bee sting can prove fatal. Anyone who discovers that he or she is allergic should immediately begin treatment to obtain immunity. The degree of sensitivity to bee venom can now be discovered through a blood test, and the treatment consists of a course of densitizing vaccinations using pure diluted venom. Eventually a tolerance level is built up, and from that time stings will cause no extreme reaction.

Bees are Good to Eat!

In some places, bees do not always survive the winter, and, in the more northerly areas of the North American prairies for example, the colonies are killed off and the hives restocked in the spring. Such colonies may each contain up to five pounds of 'mature capped brood' (bee larvae and pupae), and these have a nutritional value (they are rich in protein and vitamins A and D) which has been exploited in some places where a similar restocking procedure is necessary. A product called 'Baby Bees', consisting of mature bee pupae, fried and in soy sauce, is tinned and exported from Japan to Canada, United States of America, and elsewhere.

Experiments have been carried out at the University of Alberta in Canada into the best method of preservation and preparation of the great quantities of brood available from the Canadian prairie provinces, and these include freezing, drying, smoking, pickling, shallow frying, deep frying and baking, and the tasters preferred the brood either baked or deep-fried. Most of the tasters' reactions were favourable, and they compared the taste of the bee-brood to walnuts, pork crackling, sunflower seeds and rice crispies.

The History of Honey

Beekeeping in Antiquity
'My son, eat thou honey for it is good.'

Solomon in *Proverbs*

Man has been aware of the value of honey for many centuries. In prehistoric times, men used wild honey, for a rock painting found in Spain and thought to be at least 15,000 years old shows men taking honeycombs from a hole in a cliff.

Many paintings depicting beekeeping have been found in the Egyptian tombs, showing that the bee was important to the ancient Egyptians. They used honey in their cooking, in medicines, and made sacrificial offerings of it to their gods. It was sometimes placed in a tomb in a sealed container, presumably as food for the departed, and this honey, when discovered and opened thousands of years later, has been found to be almost as good as the day it was made.

India, China, Greece, The Roman Empire, Britain, Germany, France, Hungary, Austria, Poland, South and Central America and many other countries too, were all the home of the honey bee in olden times. Only in a few countries, such as the United States of America and Australia, were bees unknown until comparatively recently.

Honey Worldwide

At the present time, the leading honey-producing countries are the United States of America, Canada, Australia, Argentina, Mexico and China. Other leading producers are Italy, Spain, France, United Kingdom, Denmark, West Germany, East Germany (Germany was one of the main producers before World War II) and Poland. Among the countries producing smaller quantities are Yugoslavia, Czechoslovakia, Bulgaria, Austria, Switzerland, Greece, Brazil, Chile, Uruguay, Egypt, Israel, Turkey, Syria, Cyprus, New Zealand and Guatemala.

The uses of honey are as diverse as its places of origin. Today, besides its use as food and medicine, honey is used industrially in several unexpected ways — in ice cream manufacture; in cigarettes, chewing tobacco and chewing gum; in antifreeze for car radiators (it is said that if you are caught out in a sudden cold spell, with no anti-freeze in your car radiator, you can add some honey to the water as a precautionary measure because it won't freeze); as a preservative for eggs in cold storage (echoing its use in ancient Egypt in embalming); as a spray adherent; in curing pipe bowls; and as a centre for golf balls.

Honey Production in Australia

Australia is one of the world's leading honey producers, in fact she is in the top four. She is also one of the three most important honey-exporting countries, and over 18 million pounds are exported every year. There are around 16 million honey-producing bees in Australia at any one time.

But although Australia is an important source of honey today, bee-keeping is a relatively small industry, and in fact has only been considered an

industry since the late 1930s. The first true honey
bees were brought to Australia from England in
1822, and the stock has since been improved by
bees imported from Italy, Yugoslavia and North
America.

The major honey-producing state is New South
Wales; Victoria, South Australia and Western
Australia produce a certain amount, and Queens-
land and Tasmania produce relatively little.

There are around 680 different flower sources in
Australia, many from the box and gum tree
families, and the iron barks. Some of the more
important ones are yellow box, karri, stringy bark,
lucerne, white clover, blue gum, ti tree, salvation
Jane and leatherwood.

Most of the honey is obtained from the eucal-
yptus forests, where the flavours obtained are
unique to Australia. These forests also have the
advantage that they are well away from the popula-
ted and cultivated areas of the country, with the
result that the trees are not contaminated by
insecticides. In some countries, the poisoning of
bees is a major problem, and in 1967 an estimated
ten per cent of the American bee population was
seriously damaged or killed by insecticides.

Because the forests are so remote, the beekeepers
in Australia 'migrate', having found the best tem-
porary locations for the apiaries. This process of
migration from site to site continues for about eight
months of every year; for the remaining four winter
months the bees are often taken to the warmer
coastal areas.

As well as exporting honey, Australia is experi-
encing a boom in the sale of honey at home. In
1970, the consumption of honey per head had risen

from 50 g (.1lb) to 1 kilo (2.3lb), and Australia is
now second, along with Germany, in the honey
consumption table, second only to New Zealand.
Now two-thirds of the honey manufactured in
Australia is kept for home consumption.

American Honey

Bees were not introduced into Austrialia until the
nineteenth century, and the same is true of New
Zealand, Argentina, Chile and Peru. However they
made their first appearance in America in the
sixteenth century, when they were taken there by
European settlers.

The first bees to thrive in California were not
taken there until 1853, but now the state is one of
the most important beekeeping areas in the country.
It is famous for its sage, alfalfa, orange-blossom and
star thistle honeys, but other states produce equally
well-known flavours: Montana, Ohio, Michigan,
New York, Wyoming and Minnesota are known for
clover honey; Texas for its grapefruit; New England
for its raspberry; Washington and Oregon for their
fireweed. Other distinctive flavours include tupelo
tree, buckwheat, horsemint, basswood and tulip
tree. These are only a few of the plants from which
the bees make honey — there are more than 1,800
altogether. The bees also provide a valuable service
— as they do in every country — in pollinating
many agricultural crops, fruit trees, etc.

Although the United States of America is one of
the major producers of honey, her output has
decreased in recent years, from approximately
253 millions pounds per annum in 1960-64, to
200 million pounds in 1968.

Honey in Ancient Britain

Britain was once called the Isle of Honey. Honey must have been in great abundance in those far-off times, and was widely used in cooking, long before the advent of white sugar which has now, unfortunately, almost replaced it.

However, the most popular use for honey by far was in the preparation of alcoholic drinks such as mead, one of the oldest beverages in the world. It was made from the honey that remained in the combs after all the honey possible had been extracted by crushing and draining. The pieces of comb were then washed, and the honey thus obtained was used to brew mead.

In its heyday, the whole population drank mead, from the king down to the poorest peasant. Honey was widely used in all households for cooking and medicinal purposes, and the beeswax helped provide light. However, the gradual decline of mead's popularity began with the arrival of the Normans in Britain. They introduced liquor made from grapes, and Flemish immigrants in the fourteenth century introduced drinks containing hops. So after a popularity lasting at least a thousand years, mead was gradually ousted by these two newcomers which have stayed with us ever since.

However, mead has not entirely disappeared and it is still brewed in one or two places, such as St Mary's Abbey in Buckfast, Devon, where they use the honey produced by their own bees. Apart from the standard mead, there are variations such as sparkling mead which is comparable with the best sweet champagne, sack mead which is similar to sherry, and metheglin which is a spiced mead.

Professionally-made mead undergoes fermentation, but a simple mead which does not ferment can be made at home from honey and water. Make sure that you do not use a strongly flavoured honey (usually dark in colour) as the flavour will tend to dominate the mead. The golden honey from lime trees is one which makes excellent mead. 455 g (1 lb) to 680 g (1½ lb) of honey should be dissolved in 3 litres (6 pints) of water. Boil the mixture over a low heat. Skim, and continue boiling until the liquid is reduced to 2 litres (4 pints). Pour the remaining liquid into a basin, cover it and let it stand undisturbed for two or three days. It is then ready to drink. Properly fermented mead, which is made with yeast, must be left for three years to mature, if the proper flavour is to develop.

Honey in Britain Today

Honey is still produced in Britain, but in comparatively small amounts when compared with countries such as Australia and the United States of America. The poundage varies between 6.5 million and 9 million every year, and around 500,000 pounds are exported. However, consumption of honey is increasing (around 37 million pounds in 1967), and so a great deal of honey is imported, mainly from Australia, Canada, America, Mexico, Argentina, Romania and China.

Honey produced in Britain comes from a great variety of floral sources, mostly not identified. Of the identified sources, the most important and popular are clover and heather. Trees in flower, such as willow, holly, crab apple and maple, and in fruit-growing districts gooseberry, plum, pear, apple and cherry, are also frequently basic sources of nectar. Heather honey is one of the finest British honeys, and is obtained from ling, *Calluna vulgaris*, which flowers in the late summer. Beekeepers will sometimes hire a lorry to transport twenty or thirty hives up to 100 miles in order than the bees can gather some of this fine quality honey.

Honey Cookery

General Hints

Honey can safely replace sugar in almost all recipes. Not only is the flavour better, but, as I have already emphasized, honey is better for one's health. Also, cakes made with honey stay moister longer. The recipes which follow all have honey as one of their ingredients, but you can also adapt your own favourite recipes.

There are one or two points to take into account if you plan to do this. If you are making a cake, the quantity of honey needed will be only three-quarters of the amount of sugar called for. Some cooks say that no more than half of the total sweetening in a cake should be honey, or else the cake will be too heavy and soggy, and taste too strong. Also, the milk or other liquid can be reduced by a fifth for each half cupful of honey used. This takes into account the seventeen per cent of water in the honey, and retains the balance of wet and dry in the ingredients. However, all these are recommendations only, and you may find that you prefer to use all honey and no sugar, not reduce the liquid, etc. Some cooks and bakers find that to decrease the amount of milk causes the cake to crumble.

In other recipes where sugar is called for, honey can take its place measure for measure, such as puddings, pie fillings, etc. Whenever honey is used, all the ingredients should be mixed very thoroughly together. This is especially important in cake-making, where the honey should first be combined with the fat or liquid. Failure to mix the honey in properly can result in a soggy layer on top of the cake, or shading in the colour of the cake. A light, mild honey is best for use in cakes, and cakes made with honey can be cooked at the same heat as normal, which is usually 180°C/350°F (Gas Mark 4).

When measuring honey, heat the spoon in hot water, and wipe it dry quickly before dipping it into the honey jar. One level tablespoon of honey weighs approximately 30 g (1 oz); one cup of honey weighs 340 g (12 oz); 455 g (1 lb) of honey measures 1⅓ cups. If you find you are using a lot of honey (and I hope you are), you may find it more economical and convenient to buy it in 3 kilo (7 lb) tins, or even 25 kilo (56 lb) tins!

Storing Honey

Both extracted and comb honey should be stored in covered containers in a dry place at room temperature 21°C (70°F). If exposed to the air, honey tends to lose its flavour and absorb moisture. Honey kept some time tends to go darker and become stronger in flavour, but it is still usable. It may also crystallize as it gets older, or if kept in a cool place, but once again this does not affect the quality of the honey, which can be made liquid again by placing the pot in a pan of warm water until the crystals disappear.

Recipes

The following recipes demonstrate the very great variety of ways in which honey can be used in everyday cooking. In order to increase the health value of all recipes, not only those which follow, certain rules should be adopted wherever possible.

Eggs If the recipe calls for eggs, use only free-range farm eggs, not those which are battery-produced from hens fed with artificial foods.

Flour White flour is a denatured substance, with all the goodness taken our during milling. Use whole-wheat flour instead.

Sugar Some of these recipes call for sugar as well as honey. Honey on its own is very sweet — try leaving out the extra sugar. Or if you really must add sugar, use brown Barbados sugar wherever possible.

Vinegar Try using cider-apple vinegar.

Fruit juices Use only natural fruit juices, not squashes, cordials or other artificial drinks.

Rice Brown, unpolished rice has all the goodness which is no longer present in white rice, and is also much tastier.

Bread The same applies here as to flour. Use only wholemeal bread.

Butter Margarine made with vegetable oils will serve the purpose just as well in most cases.

Breakfast Dishes

Use honey instead of sugar on your breakfast cereal or porridge, on your toast or crumpets, and in your tea or coffee. Or, to give yourself an extra special start to the day, indulge in one of the honey receipes given below.

Honey French Toast

2 eggs, slightly beaten	Butter
¼ cupful milk	1 cupful honey
¼ cupful honey	2 tablespoonsful lemon
¼ teaspoonful sea salt	juice
8 slices wholemeal bread	2 tablespoonsful butter

1. Combine the beaten eggs, ¼ cupful of milk, ¼ cupful of honey and salt.

2. Dip bread in mixture and fry in butter until golden brown.

3. Combine the remaining cupful of honey, lemon juice and butter; heat. Serve over toast. Makes 4 to 6 servings.

Honey Muesli

2 tablespoonsful oats	Juice of ½ lemon
1 apple, grated	½ cupful yogurt or milk
1 tablespoonful honey	Chopped nuts

If preferred, the oats may be soaked in water overnight, though this is not really necessary. Stir all the ingredients together and serve at once. Makes 2 servings.

Note: This muesli recipe can be varied in many ways. Other cereals can be used as well as, or instead of, oats, for example craked wheat, barley kernels, and a little wheatgerm can be added. Chopped dates, pumpkin and sunflower seeds, and raisins, can all be added to make this dish a meal on its own, and slices of banana can be substituted for apple.

Overlanders' Oatmeal Breakfast Cakes

50g (2 oz) rolled oats   1 egg
25g (1 oz) wholemeal flour 1 tablespoonful Australian
¼ teaspoonful bicarbonate   honey
  of soda   Vegetable oil for frying
175ml (⅜ pint) milk
1 tablespoonful of lemon juice

1. Mix together the dry ingredients.

2. Add the lemon juice to the milk.

3. Beat the egg with honey.

4. Stir the egg mixture into the dry ingredients, then slowly add the milk. Stir well.

5. Heat a little fat in a frying pan, then drop in tablespoons of the pancake batter, well apart. Cook over a moderate heat.

6. When the top is just set and the underneath golden, turn and cook the second side. Makes 18—20 7cm (3 in.) pancakes.

Note: Serve hot with butter and honey. These pancakes are very light and make a pleasant change from the usual breakfast toast.

Sandwich Spreads

To give new interest to sandwiches, spread with butter and use any of the following fillings. Candied or creamed honey is best for sandwiches.

1. Peanut butter and honey.

2. Dates, figs and raisins mixed together with honey and lemon juice.

3. Honey, then chopped apple, or sliced or mashed banana.

4. Honey, then grated raw carrot and a sprinkling of nutmeg.

Honey and Cream Cheese

3 tablespoonsful liquid or creamed honey
100g (4 oz) cream cheese

Beat the honey and cheese together until light and fluffy. Use about 2 tablespoonsful for each sandwich. Makes enough for about 10 sandwiches.

Honey Butter

100g (4 oz) butter
4 tablespoonsful honey

Cream butter until soft, and gradually add honey. Beat well together until light and fluffy. Pot, and use on bread or biscuits. Chopped nuts or raisins can be added.

Honey and Ginger Spread

100g (4 oz) honey butter (see previous recipe)
2 tablespoonsful chopped preserved ginger
2 tablespoonsful chopped toasted almonds

Add ginger and almonds to the honey butter and mix well.

Honey Plum Butter

Wash plums and cook gently in water until soft. Sieve, and add ½ cupful of honey for each cup of pulp. Cook slowly until thick and jelly-like. Pour into hot sterilized jars, and seal.

Apricot Spread

Soak dried apricots in hot water for 5 minutes, then drain them and cut them into small pieces. Measure 1½ cupsful of honey for each cup of ground apricots, and blend thoroughly. Store in jars for at least 2 weeks. The resulting spread should be of a marmalade texture, and is delicious on toast or in hot scones.

Hot Sweets

Baked Custard

2 eggs   1½ cupsful milk
1 tablespoonful honey   Essence of vanilla

Beat eggs and honey, add milk and vanilla. Pour
into a buttered pie dish standing in a dish of water
and cook at 150°C/300°F (Gas Mark 2), until set.

Stewed Fruit

Apple, rhubarb and apple, rhubarb, prunes, plums,
peaches, apricots, pears, nectarines, cherries, and
quinces are all delicious when stewed using honey.
Do not cook the honey with the fruit, but add it
later.
Stewed apples: Peel and cut the apples. Add water, a
piece of lemon rind and a few cloves. When cooked,
take off the stove and add honey. Replace the lid
and allow to cool.

Baked Grapefruit

2 grapefruits
½ cupful honey

1. Cut grapefruit in half and remove the pips and centre.

2. Pour honey over each piece, and bake them at 150°C/300°F (Gas Mark 2) for about 15 minutes.

Christmas Pudding

¼ kilo (½ lb) butter
100g (4 oz) brown sugar
100g (4 oz) honey
4 eggs
½ cupful plain wholemeal flour
½ teaspoonful nutmeg
½ teaspoonful spice
¼ kilo (½ lb) wholemeal breadcrumbs
½ kilo (1 lb) sultanas
½ kilo (1 lb) raisins
50g (2 oz) candied peel
50g (2 oz) almonds
2 teaspoonsful brandy

1. Cream butter, sugar and honey. Add eggs one at a time, beat well.

2. Add sifted dry ingredients, then breadcrumbs and fruit. Add brandy last.

3. Place in a greased basin. Steam for 5 hours.

Sydney Honey Charlotte

25g (1 oz) butter	½ lemon
100g (4 oz) fresh whole- meal breadcrumbs	100g (4 oz) Australian honey
½ kilo (1 lb) cooking apples	1 tablespoonful water

1. Use the butter to grease a pie dish thickly.

2. Press a layer of breadcrumbs onto the sides and bottom of the dish.

3. Peel, core and slice the apples thinly, and arrange alternate layers of apples and crumbs in the dish, finishing with crumbs.

4. Grate the rind from the lemon, and squeeze out the juice. Put the lemon rind, juice, honey and water in a saucepan, and bring to the boil, stirring until well blended. Pour over the apples and crumbs.

5. Bake at 170°C/325°F (Gas Mark 3) for 1¼ hours. Serve with cream or custard. Serves 4.

Bread and Honey Pudding

½ medium wholemeal loaf	Honey
½ litre (1 pint) milk	Sultanas
Polyunsaturated margarine	Grated nutmeg

1. Slice the bread fairly thinly, spread each slice with margarine and honey, and arrange them in ovenproof greased baking dish. Sprinkle sultanas on each slice, and a little nutmeg if an extra spicy flavour is desired. Fill the dish with slices of bread, and sprinkle sultanas and nutmeg on top.

2. Warm the milk, and melt one tablespoonful of honey (or more if you want a particularly sweet pudding) in it. Pour this into the dish, making sure that all the bread is well soaked, especially that at the top.

3. Let the pudding stand for 15 minutes, and then bake in an over at 180°C/350°F (Gas Mark 4) for around 30 minutes. The top should be fairly crisp.

Note: This is a filling pudding which can be eaten either hot or cold. Cold, it tastes extra good if 2 spoonsful of plain live yogurt are served on each helping. Serves 4.

Date Pudding

60g (2½ oz) butter
3 tablespoonsful honey
2 small (or 1 large) eggs
¼ cupful milk

Vanilla essence
150g (6 oz) self-raising wholemeal flour
100g (4 oz) stoned dates
1 tablespoonful chopped walnuts

1. Beat the butter and honey to a cream, add the eggs; beat well. Add the milk and essence, then the flour.

2. Add the dates and walnuts. Steam for 1½ hours.

Meringue Apple Pie

Pastry
2 cupsful plain wholemeal
  flour
1 cupful self-raising
  wholemeal flour
¼ kilo (½ lb) butter
1 tablespoonful honey
½ cupful cold water

Filling
½ kilo (1 lb) apples
Pinch nutmeg
Juice and grated rind of
  1 lemon
2 eggs
¾ cupful milk
½ cupful honey
1 cupful cake crumbs

Pastry: Sift the flour into a basin, rub in the butter, then the honey, and mix with cold water. Make fairly stiff, roll out, and line a tart plate or pie dish.

Filling: Peel, core and thinly slice the apples, add the nutmeg and lemon and pack into a lined tart plate or pie dish. Beat the egg yolks and stir in the milk, honey and cake crumbs. Pour over the apples. Bake at 220°C/425°F (Gas Mark 7) for about 25 minutes.

Stiffly beat the egg whites with 1 tablespoonful of honey, pile on top and replace in the oven to set.

Apple Rice Meringue

2 cupsful stewed apples
1 cupful cooked brown
  rice
2 egg yolks
2 tablespoonsful honey

⅔ cupful milk
2 egg whites
pinch salt
4 tablespoonsful brown
  sugar

1. Place stewed apples in the base of a greased casserole. Place rice in a saucepan.

2. Lightly beat together the egg yolks, honey and milk. Pour over rice. Cook gently for 3 minutes stirring constantly. Pour mixture over apples.

3. Beat egg whites stiffly with salt. Fold in the sugar. Pile meringue on top of rice in casserole.

4. Bake at 180°C/350°F (Gas Mark 4) 20-25 minutes or until meringue is lightly browned. Serves 6 to 8.

Apricot Upside-Down Cake

4 tablespoonsful honey	1 teaspoonful natural vanilla
2 tablespoonsful melted butter	essence
14 dried apricot halves, soaked	2 eggs
14 walnut halves	2 cupsful self-raising wholemeal flour
100g (4 oz) butter	pinch sea salt
½ cupful brown sugar	½ cupful milk (approx.)

1. Combine honey and melted butter, and spread over the base of round cake tin.

2. Arrange drained apricot halves (round side to base of tin) and walnut pieces on top.

3. Cream butter with sugar and vanilla essence until light and fluffy. Beat in eggs one at a time, then fold in flour (which has been sifted with salt) alternately with milk.

4. Spread mixture into cake tin, and bake at 180°C/350°F (Gas Mark 4) for 40-50 minutes.

5. Unmould carefully, and serve with cream or custard sauce. Serves 6.

Honey Pudding

½ cupful honey	3 cupsful fresh wholemeal
¼ kilo (½ lb) butter	breadcrumbs
½ cupful brown sugar	4 cupsful sultanas
4 eggs	4 cupsful raisins
½ cupful plain wholemeal flour	½ cupful candied peel
½ teaspoonful nutmeg	½ cupful chopped almonds
½ teaspoonful mixed spices	2 teaspoonsful brandy

1. Cream the honey, butter and sugar. Add the eggs, one at a time, and beat well.

2. Sift the dry ingredients and add to the mixture. Then add the breadcrumbs and fruit, and almonds. Add the brandy last.

3. Place in a basin, cover securely with buttered paper and steam for approximately 5 hours.

4. Serve with Honey Butter Sauce (page 76). Serves 6 to 8.

Cold Sweets

Honey Fruit Jellies

3 teaspoonsful gelatine	3 tablespoonsful honey
⅔ cupful hot water	Sliced fruit such as bananas
¼ cupful lemon juice	Oranges and whole
⅔ cupful orange juice	strawberries

Dissolve the gelatine into the hot water. Add the fruit juices and honey, and pour into a mould. Sliced fruit can be set in the jelly, or served with the jelly. Serve with cream or custard.

Tasmanian Grape Tart

¼ kilo (½ lb) short pastry   4 teaspoonsful clear honey
½ kilo (1 lb) white grapes   4 teaspoonsful reducrrant jelly

1. Roll out the pastry to line a greased tart tin. Prick the base of the pastry with a fork, cover with a piece of greaseproof paper, and cover this with dried haricot beans or rice. Bake at 200°C/400°F (Gas Mark 6) for about 15 minutes until golden brown. Remove the beans or rice and paper and allow to cool.

2. Halve the grapes, remove pips and, if the skin is very thick, peel them. When the pastry case is cold, fill it with the grapes.

3. Melt the honey and redcurrant jelly together in a saucepan, blending them well together. Then spoon the mixture over the grapes until there is enough to set them in position. Chill. Serve with whipped cream. Serves 6 to 8.

Frozen Strawberry Salad

¼ kilo (½ lb) cream cheese   1¼ cupsful fresh crushed strawberries
2 tablespoonsful honey   ½ cupful fresh crushed pineapple

1. Blend the cream cheese and the honey. Add the fruit and stir a little. Freeze the mixture in a refrigerator tray for 2 hours.

2. To serve, cut into squares and arrange on lettuce, or pile into jelly glasses and garnish each helping with a strawberry. Serves 6.

Corroboree Honeyed Oranges

6 thin-skinned oranges	¼ kilo (½ lb) cane sugar
150ml (¼ pint) water	4 tablespoonsful clear honey
Juice of ½ lemon	100g (4 oz) stoned dates

1. Thinly pare the rind from 2 oranges, and place in a saucepan with water and lemon juice. Boil together for 10 minutes.

2. Remove from the heat, add the sugar and stir until dissolved. Simmer until syrupy, and stir in the honey.

3. Remove all the peel and pith from the oranges, and plunge them into boiling water for 3 to 4 minutes. Drain the oranges and place in a shallow ovenproof dish with the dates.

4. Strain the orange and honey syrup over the top. Bake at 190°C/375°F (Gas Mark 5) for 20 to 25 minutes. Serve either hot or cold, with whipped cream. Serves 6.

Pineapple Whip

1 fresh pineapple	3 tablespoonsful honey
1 cupful water	Juice of ½ lemon
1 avocado	

Cut the pineapple into small cubes. Add water, avocado, honey and lemon juice. Blend until smooth and serve at once. Serves 4 to 6.

Raspberries and Honey

Hull raspberries and place in a deep dish. Cover with cream, squeeze over a few drops of lemon juice, and pour on some honey. Allow to stand for a few minutes, and then stir gently until all the items are well mixed.

Outback Honey Mousse

1 kilo (2 lb) eating apples	3 tablespoonsful honey
25g (1 oz) butter	2 teaspoonsful gelatine
¼ litre (½ pint) double cream	

1. Peel, core and chop the apples and cook in a covered pan with butter and water over a low heat until soft. Take off the lid and continue cooking quickly until the *purée* is just firm. Take off the heat.

2. Stir in the honey and gelatine soaked in 2 tablespoonsful of cold water. Stir until dissolved, then leave to cool.

3. Whip the cream until just stiff, fold in the apple *purée* and pile into a glass dish. Leave in a cold place for 2 hours, and decorate with cream and nuts. Serves 6.

Honey Apricot Custard

2 tablespoonsful chopped dried apricots	½ cupful honey
1½ cupsful milk	4 eggs
½ cupful evaporated milk	Pinch sea salt
	Few drops vanilla essence

1. Cover apricots with a little hot water and allow to stand 15 minutes. Drain, and divide between 4 greased custard moulds.

2. Combine the milks with the honey and heat until lukewarm.

3. Beat eggs lightly, then combine with milk, salt and vanilla essence. Strain through a fine sieve, and pour into moulds.

4. Stand moulds in a shallow dish containing hot water. Bake at 180°C/350°F (Gas Mark 4) for 30-35 minutes, or until a knife inserted comes out clean.

5. Serve chilled, and topped with cream. Serves 4.

Honey Ice Cream

2 large eggs, separated	½ teaspoonful lemon rind
½ cupful honey	1 cupful cream
¼ cupful lemon juice	

1. Beat egg whites until they hold their shape. Continue beating while adding honey gradually.

2. Beat egg yolks until thick and lemon coloured. Fold beaten yolks, lemon juice and rind into whites.

3. Beat cream until stiff. Fold gently into egg mixture.

4. Pour into chilled refrigerator tray. Freeze at lowest temperature for several hours.

5. Serve in chilled dishes, garnish with shavings of carob. Serves 4.

Cakes and Breads

Apricot Nut Bread

½ cupful honey
½ kilo (1 lb) apricots
3 cupsful self-raising whole-meal flour
½ teaspoonful bicarbonate of soda

¾ cupful milk
2 tablespoonsful butter
1 egg
½ cupful chopped nuts

1. Cook the apricots in a ½ cupful of water until tender. Rub through a sieve and boil until there is 1 cupful of pulp.

2. Sift dry the ingredients, rub in the butter.

3. Beat egg well. Add the milk, egg, apricot pulp and honey mix into a light dough. Pour into a well greased oven tin 20cm × 15cm (8in. × 6in.), bake at 220°C/425°F (Gas Mark 7) for 45 minutes.

Hot Cross Buns

15g (½ oz) yeast	½ kilo (1 lb) plain wholemeal flour
1 tablespoonful honey	
¼ litre (½ pint) milk	1 teaspoonful mixed spice
1 egg	50g (2 oz) currants

1. Cream yeast and honey; warm the milk and pour in a beaten egg.

2. Sieve the flour and spice into a basin and warm. Make a well in the centre, pour in the yeast and milk mixture and beat to a smooth dough. Allow to rise in a warm place for 1 hour.

3. Knead in currants lightly on a floured board. Shape buns (1 dozen) and mark cross with a floured knife. Allow to rise for 15 minutes.

4. Bake at 230°C/450°F (Gas Mark 8) for 15 to 20 minutes. Brush with a glaze made from 1 teaspoonful of honey and 2 teaspoonsful of water.

Walnut Cake

100g (4 oz) butter	2 tablespoonsful honey
1 cupful brown sugar	½ cupful milk
2 eggs	½ teaspoonful vanilla
1½ cupsful self-raising wholemeal flour	½ cupful chopped walnuts
½ teaspoonful cinnamon	

1. Cream the butter and sugar, add the egg yolks and beat in well.

2. Sift the flour and cinnamon. Mix the honey, milk and vanilla.

3. Add the dry ingredients alternately with the liquids, mixing lightly. Add the nuts.

4. Beat the egg whites until stiff, and fold them lightly into the mixture. Bake in a 18cm (7 in.) round tin at 180°C/350°F (Gas Mark 4) for about 40 minutes.

5. When cold, ice with lemon or honey icing and sprinkle with chopped walnuts.

Honey Icing

1½ cupsful honey   1 egg white
½ teaspoonful vanilla

1. Cook the honey to 130°C/250°F or until it will spin a thread or make a soft ball when dropped into cold water.

2. Beat the egg white.

3. Pour the syrup in a thin stream over the beaten egg white, continuing to beat until all the syrup is added and the icing stands in peaks. Add vanilla and spread on the cake.

Honey Fruit Cake

2½ cupsful plain wholemeal flour

2 teaspoonsful baking powder

2 teaspoonsful mixed spices

¼ kilo (½ lb) butter

1 cupful honey

5 eggs

100g (4 oz) mixed peel

2 cupsful chopped raw peanuts

1 cupful chopped almonds

2 cupsful currants

2 cupsful seedless raisins

1 cupful dates

¼ kilo (½ lb) candied cherries

100g (4 oz) crystalized pineapple

1. Sift flour and divide into 2 equal parts. To one add the baking powder and mixed spices, and sift twice more.

2. Cream butter well. Add honey. Add well beaten egg yolks. Add sifted dry ingredients gradually. Fold in stiffly beaten egg whites.

3. Roll nuts and fruits (except cherries and pineapple) in the remaining flour. Add to the dough mixture.

4. Add the cherries and pineapple. Bake in a 23cm (9 in.) tin at 140°C/275°F (Gas Mark 1) for 2½ hours or more.

Honey Sponge

3 eggs   100g (4 oz) self-raising
¾ cupful honey   wholemeal flour
                                4 teaspoonsful cold water

1. Beat the whites of 2 eggs with honey until stiff;
   beat yolks with the remaining egg. Gently stir
   into the first mixture.

2. Fold in the sifted flour, and lightly mix in water.
   Bake in well greased sandwich tins at 180°C/
   350°F (Gas Mark 4) for 30 minutes.

Filling: 2 tablespoonsful each of butter, honey and
vanilla beaten to a cream.

Mixed Nut Loaf

1 cupful chopped apricots	3 cupsful self-raising whole-
1 cupful chopped mixed nuts	meal flour
1 cupful sultanas	4 tablespoonsful honey
½ cupful brown sugar	2 eggs
	6 tablespoonsful milk

Topping
½ cupful mixed whole nuts (shelled)
¼ cupful brown sugar
2 tablespoonsful water

1. Place the dried apricots in a bowl and cover with boiling water. Leave for 10 minutes and then drain.

2. Mix the apricots, nuts, sultanas, sugar and flour together in a bowl. Place the honey in a basin with eggs and milk and beat together. Add to the flour mixture and mix well. Add a little more milk if necessary.

3. Pour the mixture into a loaf tin which has been greased and lined. Bake at 150°C/300°F (Gas Mark 2) for about 1¼ hours.

4. When cooked the loaf should have begun to shrink from the sides of the tin. Turn out and cool.

Topping
5. Toast nuts lightly.

6. Place sugar and water in a saucepan over a moderate heat and stir until dissolved. Bring to the boil and boil for one minute. Remove from heat add the nuts, and stir to coat.

7. Spread over the top of the cooled loaf.

8. Serve the loaf sliced and buttered. Makes 12 to 16 slices.

Apricot Cinnamon Cake

2 cupsful self-raising whole- 1 cupful soft brown sugar
meal flour   1 cupful dried apricots
1 teaspoonful cinnamon 1 tablespoonful honey
Pinch sea salt   4 tablespoonsful milk
100g (4 oz) butter   2 eggs

Topping
½ cupful chopped almonds 3 tablespoonsful honey
25g (1 oz) butter

1. Sift together the dry ingredients. Rub in the butter. Then add the sugar, and apricots which have been chopped.

2. Blend honey with the milk and beaten eggs. Stir lightly into the dry ingredients.

3. Pour into a greased and lined 20cm (8 in) fruit cake tin, and bake at 180°C/350°F (Gas Mark 4) for 1½ hours.

4. Cool for a few minutes in tin before turning out to cool. When cold, top with topping.

Topping
5. Heat all the topping ingredients until the butter is melted. Then boil for 3 to 5 minutes. Spread over cake.

Brisbane Cake

Filling

1½ cupsful chopped dates	3 tablespoonsful honey
½ cupful boiling water	1 teaspoonful grated lemon rind

2 cupsful self-raising wholemeal flour	1 egg, beaten
	1 tablespoonful honey
Pinch sea salt	2 tablespoonsful milk
75g (3 oz) butter	2 teaspoonsful grated lemon rind
⅓ cupful brown sugar	

1. Prepare filling by mixing ingredients well together. Allow to cool.

2. Sift flour and salt. Rub in butter, and add sugar.

3. Beat the egg, honey and milk together. Add the lemon rind.

4. Pour into dry ingredients and mix to a firm dough. Turn on to a floured board and knead.

5. Divide dough into two. Roll each piece into an 20cm (8 in.) circle.

6. Place one portion in a greased and lined 20cm (8 in.) cake tin. Lightly press edges partly up sides of tin.

7. Spread filling over dough in tin. Cover with second portion of dough. Pinch edges together and prick top with a fork. Bake at 180°C/350°F (Gas Mark 4) for 40 to 45 minutes.

8. Allow to cool. Dust top with icing sugar. Makes 6-8 wedges.

Cheesecake

1½ cupful wholemeal
  biscuit crumbs
½ cupful chopped walnuts
75g (3 oz) butter, melted
3 cupful creamed cottage
  cheese
3 eggs

½ cupful honey
¼ cupful brown sugar
2 tablespoonsful whole-
  meal flour
Whipped Cream
Strawberries

1. Combine biscuit crumbs, chopped walnuts and melted butter. Press firmly over base and sides of a greased 18cm (7 in.) spring form tin. Chill while preparing mixture.

2. Push cheese through a sieve and beat in eggs one at a time. Add honey and sugar. Beat until smooth.

3. Fold in the flour and turn mixture into the crumb crust. Bake at 180°C/350°F (Gas Mark 4) for 1 hour.

4. Leave cheesecake in oven with heat turned off, and door open, until quite cold.

5. To serve, decorate with whipped cream and strawberries. Makes 6 to 8 wedges.

Biscuits, Scones and Slices

Honey Oat Cookies

25g (1 oz) plain wholemeal flour
25g (1 oz) rolled oats
25g (1 oz) brown sugar
50g (2 oz) polyunsaturated margarine

1 tablespoonful honey
Pinch cinnamon
Cherries and hazelnuts to decorate

1. Sieve flour into a bowl. Add the rolled oats, sugar, margarine and honey. Knead together until smooth.

2. Divide the mixture into walnut-sized pieces, roll into balls, place on a greased baking tray and slightly flatten.

3. Decorate with a piece of cherry or half hazelnut. Bake at 190°C/375°F (Gas Mark 5) for 10 to 15 minutes, until golden brown. Makes 24 biscuits.

Honey Scones

1 tablespoonful butter	Enough milk to mix
3 cupsful self-raising whole-meal flour	1 teaspoonful grated orange rind
1 teaspoonful honey	

Rub butter into the flour, then add honey and milk. Mix, roll and cut into scones. Cook on a baking sheet in a hot oven at 230°C/450°F (Gas Mark 8) for 10 minutes. An egg may be included if desired.

Note: Do not mix too dry.

Honey Raisin Bars

75g (3 oz) butter	1 teaspoonful baking powder
6 tablespoonsful honey	150g (6 oz) stoned raisins
3 eggs	100g (4 oz) chopped hazelnuts or walnuts
150g (6 oz) plain wholemeal flour	

1. Cream together butter and honey and beat in the eggs 1 at a time.

2. Sift in the flour and baking powder, and stir in the raisins and nuts.

3. Spread on a greased rectangular baking sheet 22cm × 30cm (9 in. × 12 in.) and bake in the oven at 180°C/225°F (Gas Mark 4) for 30 minutes or until golden brown.

4. Cool in the tin and cut into bars. These bars keep well and are 'chewy' and moist.

Chocolate Chip Biscuits

½ cupful butter
½ cupful butter
1 small egg
150g (6 oz) self-raising
  wholemeal flour

½ teaspoonful vanilla
  essence
½ cupful grated chocolate
¼ cupful chopped nuts

1. Cream the butter and honey until light and fluffy. Add egg and beat well.

2. Add the flour to the butter mixture, add the vanilla and blend well.

3. Fold in the chocolate and nuts, chill and drop by teaspoonfuls on to a buttered baking sheet. Bake at 180°C/350°F (Gas Mark 4) for 12 to 15 minutes.

Wholemeal Honey Bran Cookies

100g (4 oz) butter
1 tablespoonful honey melted
100g (4 oz) cane sugar
1 egg
150g (6 oz) self-raising wholemeal flour

½ teaspoonful each cin-
amon, ground ginger and
spice

1. Cream butter, honey and sugar, add the beaten egg, and then the flour with the other dried ingredients, mix well.

2. Turn out on to a board well floured with wholemeal flour, roll out fairly thin, cut into shapes, brush with milk and put half a blanched almond on top.

3. Bake on a greased baking sheet at 180°C/350°F (Gas Mark 4) for about 25 minutes.

Alice Springs Honey Biscuits

125g (5 oz) wholemeal flour 1 teaspoonful baking
25g (1 oz) oatmeal   powder
75g (3 oz) butter   2 tablespoonsful thin
1 tablespoonful milk   honey

1. Place the flour and oatmeal in a basin, add the baking powder. Mix well and rub in the butter until the mixture resembles bread crumbs.

2. Stir in the honey and milk to bind the mixture. Knead lightly and roll out thinly on a floured board until it is less than 5mm (¼ in.) thick.

3. Cut out with fluted biscuit cutters and place on a baking sheet. Bake at 180°C/350°F (Gas Mark 4) for 15 to 20 minutes. Cool and serve with butter. Makes about 12 to 15 biscuits.

Honey and Chocolate Fingers

⅔ cupful dark chocolate,   ¾ cupful plain wholemeal
    grated   flour
100g (4 oz) butter   2 teaspoonsful baking
Pinch sea salt   powder
1 teaspoonful natural vanilla   ½ cupful finely chopped
    essence   walnuts
¾ cupful honey   2 eggs, slightly beaten

1. Place chocolate in a double saucepan with
   butter, salt and vanilla essence. Stir over low
   heat until chocolate and butter have melted.

2. Stir in honey, sift flour with baking powder
   twice, then fold into mixture. Mix in walnuts
   and eggs, combining well. Turn mixture into a
   greased slab tin.

3. Bake at 170°C/325°F (Gas Mark 3) for 40-45
   minutes, or until done when tested.

4. Cool in tin, then cut into finger-length pieces. If
   desired, top with whipped cream and grated
   chocolate. Makes 24 fingers.

Apricot Honey Cookies

100g (4 oz) butter   2 cupsful self-raising
3 tablespoonsful honey   wholemeal flour
¼ cupful brown sugar   1 tablespoonful cocoa
1 egg   1 cupful chopped dried
                                     apricots

1. Cream butter with honey and sugar until light
   and fluffy. Beat in egg.

2. Sift together the flour and cocoa. Fold into mixture.

3. Add the chopped apricots. Make mixture into balls. Place on greased oven tray and bake at 180°C/350°F (Gas Mark 4) for approximately 12-15 minutes.

4. When cool, ice with chocolate icing and decorate with a cherry. Makes 40 cookies.

Honey Biscuits

½ cupful brown sugar
1 egg, beaten
⅓ cupful honey
2 cupsful plain wholemeal
  flour

¼ teaspoonful cinnamon
1 teaspoonful baking
  powder
100g (4 oz) butter
Pinch sea salt

Filling

2 tablespoonsful butter
2 teaspoonsful grated lemon
  rind
2 cupsful sifted icing sugar

2 tablespoonsful honey
squeeze lemon juice

1. Cream together butter and sugar. Mix in beaten
   egg and honey.

2. Sift the dry ingredients twice, and fold into
   creamed mixture. Combine thoroughly.

3. Roll teaspoonsful of mixture into balls and place
   on a greased tray. Flatten slightly with a fork.
   Bake at 180°C/350°F (Gas Mark 4) for about 15
   minutes.

4. To make the filling, cream together the butter,
   lemon rind and sugar. Mix in the honey and
   lemon juice.

5. Join the biscuits together with the filling. Makes
   48 biscuits.

Savouries

Honey Cinnamon Toast

Toast slices of bread on one side. While still hot,

butter the untoasted side of the bread. Spread the buttered side with honey. Sprinkle cinnamon on top. Place the slices under a grill flame until the bread is well browned and the topping is well blended.

Honey Cheese

1 part honey to
2 parts grated cheese

Hot buttered toast

Mix honey and cheese to a paste. Spread on hot buttered toast and put back under the grill for a minute or two to melt slightly.

Potato Cakes

1 kilo (2 lb) potatoes
¼ kilo (½ lb) plain wholemeal flour
1 tablespoonful butter

1 teaspoonful yeast
2 teaspoonful honey
Raisins

1. Cook the potatoes in their jackets, peel, mash, and mix with flour, butter, yeast, honey and a few raisins. Put into a basin and leave to rise for at least 1 hour.

2. Divide into small oven buns and bake at 200°C/400°F (Gas Mark 6). Makes 24.

Note: This makes a useful supper dish with cheese and chutney.

Honey Chutney

1¼ kilo (2½ lb) cooking apples	¼ teaspoonful cayenne pepper
150g (6 oz) seedless raisins	2 medium sized onions
4 tablespoonsful honey	½ teaspoonful sea salt
150ml (¼ pint) cider vinegar	Juice of 3 lemons (made up to 150ml (¼ pint) with water)
1 green pepper	
1 tablespoonful chopped stem ginger	

Wash fruit and vegetables, remove peel, core and chop. Add all other ingredients and simmer till thick. Seal in hot jars. Makes 1½ kilo (3 lb) of chutney.

Adelaide Honey Pie

¼ kilo (½ lb) short pastry	2 eggs
¼ kilo (½ lb) cottage cheese	Pinch powdered cinnamon
50g (2 oz) honey	25g (1 oz) chopped hazelnuts

1. Line a pie plate or flan ring with pastry. Sieve cottage cheese and blend with honey, beaten eggs and cinnamon.

2. Fill the pastry case and bake in the over at 180°C/350°F (Gas Mark 4) for 30 minutes. Sprinkle with chopped nuts and a little more cinnamon. Serves 8.

Fruit Cole Slaw

1 cupful sliced fresh apricots   1 tablespoonful cider
2/3 cupful grapefruit sections   vinegar
2 cupsful shredded cabbage   ¼ teaspoonful sea salt
¼ cupful thick sour cream   2 tablespoonsful honey

1. Dice apricots and prepare grapefruit. Combine
   with the cabbage.

2. Blend together the remaining ingredients and
   pour over the mixture. Toss lightly until well
   mixed. Serves 4.

Cream Cheese Whip

75g (3 oz) cream cheese
2 tablespoonsful honey
3 tablespoonsful live yogurt

Blend cream cheese and yogurt, add honey, and
beat until light and fluffy. Serves 6 to 8, when used
as a topping for fresh fruit.

Vegetables Baked in Honey

½ cupful honey
2 tablespoonsful butter
¾ kilo (1½ lb) vegetables (carrots, parsnips, turnips or
onions)

Combine the honey and butter. Pour over the
vegetables. Bake at 190°C/375°F (Gas Mark 5) for
40 to 60 minutes, turning occasionally to glaze
evenly. Serves 6.

Sauces

Honey Butter Sauce

½ cupful honey
50g (2 oz) butter

Place honey and butter in a saucepan and stir until heated and the butter is melted. Serve warm with a pudding.

Butterscotch Sauce

1 well beaten egg yolk
¼ cupful butter
¼ cupful water

⅔ cupful brown sugar
⅓ cupful honey

Combine all the ingredients and mix well; cook in a double saucepan until thick, stirring frequently. Beat before using. Serve hot or cold over ice-cream.

Honey Cream Sauce

⅓ cupful whipping cream
1 teaspoonful lemon juice
¼ to ½ cupful honey

Beat cream until thick. Beat in honey and lemon juice.

Orange Honey Sauce

½ cupful honey
1 teaspoonful grated orange rind
¼ cupful orange juice

Mix ingredients until well blended. Makes ¾ cupful.

Salad Dressing

Beat well together one part each of lemon juice and clear honey and two parts olive oil. Add an egg white, stiffly beaten.

Apple Sauce

6 green apples   Juice of half lemon
½ cupful honey   3 cloves
½ cupful water

1. Peel, core and quarter apples.

2. Place honey, water, lemon juice and cloves in a saucepan. Bring to the boil.

3. Add apples and place lid on saucepan. Simmer gently until apples are cooked.

4. Remove cloves. Serve with pork or poultry. Makes approximately 2 cups.

Honey French Dressing

½ cupful vegetable oil	½ teaspoonful paprika
½ cupful lemon juice	½ teaspoonful sea salt
½ cupful honey	1 clove garlic, crushed

1. Place ingredients in a tightly covered jar and shake vigorously just before using.

2. Keep for further use, but do not refrigerate. Makes 1½ cups dressing.

Choco Honey Sauce

3 cupsful grated semi-sweet chocolate
½ cupful cream
4 tablespoonsful honey

1. Melt chocolate in the top of a double saucepan.

2. Gradually add cream and honey, beating well until smooth.

3. Serve over vanilla ice-cream. Makes approximately 1¾ cupsful sauce.

Raisin Sauce

1 cupful raisins	1 tablespoonful cornflour
¼ cupful honey	1 cupful water
Grated rind of 1 lemon	2 tablespoonsful butter
2 tablespoonsful lemon juice	2 tablespoonsful rum
Pinch sea salt	

1. Combine the raisins, honey, lemon rind, juice and salt; blend the cornflour with the water and add.

2. Bring all the ingredients to the boil, stirring gently.
   Simmer for 4-5 minutes.

3. Stir in the butter and rum. It can be reheated for later use. Serve hot with ice-cream.

Rum Pineapple Sauce

2 tablespoonsful cornflour   2 tablespoonsful honey
1 large can crushed pineapple   ¼ cupful rum
2 tablespoonsful butter   Toasted coconut
2 tablespoonsful lemon juice

1. Mix the cornflour with the crushed pineapple. Stir till boiling.

2. Add butter, lemon, honey and rum.

3. Chill and serve over ice-cream. Sprinkle with toasted coconut. Makes approximately 2¼ cupsful.

Honey Avocado Dressing

½ cupful orange juice   ½ cupful mayonnaise
2 tablespoonsful lemon juice   ½ teaspoonful sea salt
2 tablespoonsful honey   Dash hot pepper sauce

1. Combine all ingredients together thoroughly. Chill before use.

2. Halve avocado, remove stone, and fill with chilled dressing. Serve immediately. Makes 1½ cups.

Lemon Mint Sauce

½ cupful honey	¼ cupful chopped fresh
½ cupful lemon juice	mint, or
4 tablespoonsful lukewarm	1 tablespoonful dried mint
water	1 teaspoonful melted butter

1. Blend all ingredients except mint in a saucepan. Heat thoroughly over low heat. Mix in mint.

2. Serve warm, adding the melted butter. Makes 1¼ cupsful sauce.

Jams and Preserves

When used for *preserving*, honey keeps the full flavour of the fruit. A pale, mild honey should be used, as the taste is less strong.

Syrup ⅓ honey to ⅔ water. Dissolve the honey in warm water and cover each jar of prepared fruit with syrup.

Apricots Take 1 hour to bring to 71°C (160°F). Maintain as near as possible for 2½ hours.

Pears Bring slowly to 93°C (200°F), then let it fall to 82°C (180°F). Maintain as near as possible for 2½ hours. Count time from the moment 93°C (200°F) is first reached.

Peaches (Freestone) Bring slowly to 82°C (180°F) and allow the temperature to fall to 71°C (160°F) and maintain as near as possible for 2½ hours, counting time from when 82°C (180°F) is reached.

Plums (Greengage) Bring slowly to 82°C (180°F). Maintain as near as possible for 2½ hours.

Apples and Rhubarb Same method as for plums.

Mild-flavoured honey should be used in *jam-making*, and less honey is needed than sugar. If the fruit juice is rich in pectin, use ¾ cupful of honey to a cupful of fruit pulp.

For fruits less rich in pectin, use only slightly less honey than the amounts of sugar called for in the recipe. These instructions only apply when converting standard recipes; the following recipes have the correct proportions of honey and sugar listed in the ingredients.

Honey Apricot Jam

1½ kilo (3 lb) stoned apricots	Juice of 2 lemons
575g (1¼ lb) honey	¼ cupful split kernels

1. Cut up the apricots and stand overnight with the honey and lemon juice.

2. Cook until the mixture gels when tested on a cold saucer, adding the split blanched kernels 10 minutes before removing from the heat.

Melbourne Pineapple and Orange Conserve

1 large pineapple, peeled anf finely chopped
4 thin-skinned oranges, finely chopped (pips removed)
¼ kilo (½ lb) honey
1¼ kilo (2½ lb) granulated brown sugar

1. Place the prepared fruits in a saucepan or preserving pan, and add a little of the juice, just to moisten the fruit.

2. Allow to simmer over a gentle heat for 20 to 25 minutes, until the orange peel is soft. Add the honey and sugar, and stir to dissolve.

3. Bring to the boil, and boil for a further 20 minutes.

4. Pour into hot jam jars and seal. Label when cold. Yields approximately 5 to 6 half kilo (1 lb) jars.

Note: Any excess juice obtained from the fruits during preparation must be measured, as this can upset the setting point of the conserve. This recipe differs from the standard jam recipe in that the consistency of the conserve is rather more liquid, and the flavour sweeter.

Honey Orange Marmalade

2 medium oranges
¼ medium grapefruit
⅓ lemon
4¾ cupsful water per ½ kilo (1 lb) of fruit

¼ kilo (½ lb) cane sugar per ½ kilo (1 lb) of fruit and liquid
¼ kilo (½ lb) honey per ½ kilo (1 lb) of fruit and liquid

1. Cut the fruit into very thin slices, cut each slice into eighths. Remove seeds, pithy inner portion and about half the orange rind. Add the water to the fruit and let it stand in the refrigerator for 24 hours.

2. Boil steadily for about 1 hour, or until the rind is tender and slightly translucent. Weigh the fruit and liquid and add the required amount of sugar.

3. Boil slowly until it reaches 101°C (214°F), add the required amount of honey, and cook to 103°C (218°F). Remove from the stove, and pour into hot sterilized jars. Yields approximately 1 litre (2 pints).

Candies

Honey Toffee

Honey makes very fine toffee. Boil the honey until it hardens when dropped into water. Pull until it becomes white. A ½ kilo (1 lb) requires 20 minutes boiling and stirring. Great care must be exercised not to burn the honey.

Honey Marzipan

100g (4 oz) ground almonds	Vanilla and almond essence
1 tablespoonful thick honey	Natural colouring as liked

1. Mix almonds to a firm paste with the honey, adding a few drops of vanilla and almond essence.

2. Divide the mixture into 2 or 3 portions. Leave one portion uncoloured. Add a few drops of colouring to the remainder, use green or yellow; work in smoothly. Wrap each piece in polythene until required.

Walnut Bon-bons

Roll honey marzipan into small balls and sandwich between 2 walnut halves, using a very little apricot jam to hold the nuts in place.

Down-Under Sunshine Candy

2 teaspoonsful honey	½ teaspoonful grated lemon rind
¾ cupful dried apricots	
¾ cupful shredded coconut	½ teaspoonful grated orange rind
2 teaspoonsful orange juice	

1. Wash apricots, cover with boiling water and let stand for 5 minutes.

2. Drain, then mince or finely chop apricots and coconut, add the remining ingredients and knead until blended. If the mixture seems a little dry, add more orange juice.

3. Shape into 2cm (1 in.) balls. Roll in sugar, dessicated coconut or finely chopped nuts.

Creamy Caramels

50g (2 oz) butter	1 cupful brown sugar
2 tablespoonsful honey	1 large can condensed milk

1. Melt butter, add sugar and allow to dissolve.

2. Add honey and milk and keep on low light until boiling point is reached. Boil 15-20 minutes (or until a ball is formed when dropped into cold water), stirring all the time.

3. Pour into greased tin and when almost cold, mark into squares. When cold cut into squares.

Honeycomb

3 tablespoonsful honey	15g (½ oz) butter
5 tablespoonsful granulated brown sugar	1 teaspoonful wine vinegar
4 tablespoonsful water	1 teaspoonful bicarbonate of soda

1. Put honey, sugar, water, butter and vinegar into saucepan.

2. Heat slowly, stirring until sugar dissolves and butter melts. Bring to boil. Cover pan. Boil gently for 2 minutes.

3. Uncover and continue to boil without stirring for about 5 minutes (or until a little of the mixture, dropped into a cup of cold water, separates into hard and brittle threads).

4. Draw pan away from heat. Stir in bicarbonate of soda (mixture will rise in pan). Pour into small buttered tin.

Note: As honeycomb does not keep well and very quickly gets sticky, it should be made and eaten on the same day.

Drinks

Honey Fruit Punch

4 tablespoonsful honey	½ cupful lemon juice
1 cupful orange juice	2 cupsful water
½ cupful grapefruit juice	1 tablespoonful cane sugar

Blend ingredients well and chill. Serve in tall glasses with ½ a slice of orange to garnish.

Riverina Fruit Cocktails

1 small ripe lemon	6 tablespoonful olive oil
150g (6 oz) black grapes	3 tablespoonful honey
2 thin-skinned oranges	Seasoning
2 tablespoonful lemon juice	Curls of orange rind
2 teaspoonful grated orange rind	

1. Peel oranges, remove pith, divide into segments.

2. Cut melon into quarters, discard the pips, and carefully remove the flesh from the peel. Cut into large dice, and combine with the grape and orange segments.

3. Mix the lemon juice, orange rind, oil, honey and seasoning together and pour over the fruits. Chill well. Serve in cocktail glasses, garnished with curls of orange rind. Serves 6.

Honey Egg Flip

1 teaspoonful honey	Milk
1 egg	Natural flavouring

Beat the egg, add the honey, fill the glass with milk and add the vanilla (or other flavouring). Can be served warm or cold.

Honey and Oatmeal

2 tablespoonsful oatmeal
3 tablespoonsful honey
Juice of 2 lemons

1. Put the oatmeal in a litre (2 pint) jug nearly full
    of fresh boiling water. Cover and stand for 24
    hours.

2. In another jug dissolve honey in a little boiling
    water with the lemon juice. Strain the oatmeal
    water into this, and it is now ready to drink.

Note: Similar drinks can also be made with pearl
barley instead of oatmeal, and lime juice instead of
lemon juice.

Wallaroo Fruit and Vegetable Cup

1 firm eating apple
1 piece of cucumber, approx. 5cm (2 in)
1 medium carrot, chopped
½ litre (1 pint) water
2 tablespoonsful clear honey
Few sprigs mint

Place all the ingredients in a goblet blender and
switch on to high speed for 15 to 30 seconds. Strain
the mixture through a nylon sieve into a jug. Add
ice cubes and serve in tall glasses. Serves 2 to 3.

Pep Cocktail

1 teaspoonful honey
Juice of 1 orange

Juice of 1 lemon
1 egg yolk

Shake all the ingredients together well.

Orange Honey Mint

½ cupful honey
6 oranges
1 bunch crushed mint leaves

1½ litre (3 pints) ginger ale
  or soda water
1 cupful water
Crushed ice

1. Grate the rinds from the oranges, place in a saucepan with the water, mint leaves and honey.

2. Bring to the boil, cook for 5 minutes. Strain through a fine wire strainer or piece of muslin. Add the orange juice. Chill. Serve in tall glasses with ginger ale or soda water, crushed ice and mint sprigs. Serves 8.

Canberra Clown's Punch

3 tablespoonsful clear honey
3 teaspoonsful orange rind
¼ litre (½ pint) orange
  juice

¾ litre (1½ pints) milk
2 individual blocks vanilla
  ice-cream
Orange slices

1. Mix honey, orange rind and orange juice together in a large basin.

2. Whisk the milk and then the ice-cream. Pour into tall glasses and serve chilled with slice of orange and straws. Makes 6 glasses.

Banana Egg Nog

2 cupsful milk   1 egg
3 ripe bananas   Nutmeg
2 tablespoonsful honey

Combine all ingredients except nutmeg in a blender,
pour into glasses and top with a sprinkling of
nutmeg - and serve. Makes 4 glasses.

Hobart Mulled Cider

1 large bottle cider   Pinch of allspice
2cm (1 in.) stick cinnamon   3 whole cloves
pinch of nutmeg   ¼ cupful honey

Combine cider, spices and honey. Heat slowly, and
simmer for 15 minutes. Serve hot. Add a slice of
orange or lemon.

Honey Milk Shake

2 cupsful milk   Pinch of cinnamon
2 tablespoonsful honey   Pinch of ginger

Combine all ingredients together thoroughly. Serve
well chilled. Makes one milk shake.

Honey Spiced Tea

2cm (1 in.) stick cinnamon   2 teaspoonsful dried tea
Pinch of allspice   2 tablespoonsful lemon
Pinch of ground cloves   juice
6 cupsful water   ½ cupful honey

1. Add spices to water and simmer for 10 minutes.

2. Pour this infusion slowly over the tea. Strain. Add lemon juice and honey. Serve hot. Makes 6 cups.

Iced Honeyed Coffee

2 cupsful strong hot coffee   2 tablespoonsful honey
1 small stick cinnamon

1. Place the hot coffee and cinnamon stick in a pot, and allow to stand until cold.

2. Remove the cinnamon, and add honey. Stir until dissolved.

3. Pour into tall glasses that are half filled with ice. Top each glass with a tablespoonful of whipped cream. Makes 2 glasses.

Orange Honey Nog

1 tablespoonful honey   ½ cupful orange juice
1 egg

Blend all ingredients together with an egg beater or blender for a few seconds. Makes one serving.

Beeswax in Homemade Polish and Shoe Cream

Polish for furniture and floors

½ kilo (1 lb) beeswax
2 litres (4 pints) water
1 litre (2 pints) turpentine

75g (3 oz) bicarbonate of
   potash
Small cake of Castile soap

Shred the beeswax and soap and dissolve in the water with the potash over a gentle heat, in a saucepan. Pour the mixture into a large basin and add the turpentine, stirring continuously until almost cold, when the mixture will become as a cream. The polish may be coloured by adding ochre or dye, and can be stored in jars.

Furniture or Shoe Cream

¼ kilo (½ lb) beeswax
25g (1 oz) white wax
25g (1 oz) Castile soap

1 litre (2 pints) turpentine
1 litre (2 pints) rainwater

Cut all the ingredients into pieces and boil them together in the rainwater for 20 minutes. Allow to cool, and when nearly cold, add the turpentine and shake until a good cream is formed.

Waterproofing for Shoes

100g (4 oz) beeswax
100g (4 oz) resin

½ litre (1 pint) linseed oil
150ml (¼ pint) turpentine

Melt wax and resin together over a gentle heat and stir in the oil. Remove from the heat and add the

turpentine. When you wish to use this water-
proofing, melt the amount needed and rub it well into
the leather.

Index